Ransom Neutron Stars
Ben's Jerk Chicken Van
by Cath Jones
Illustrated by Mia Underwood

Published by Ransom Publishing Ltd.
Unit 7, Brocklands Farm, West Meon, Hampshire GU32 1JN, UK
www.ransom.co.uk

ISBN   978 178591 428 7
First published in 2017
Reprinted 2018

There is a reading comprehension quiz available for this book in the popular
Accelerated Reader® software system. For information about ATOS, Accelerated
Reader, quiz points and reading levels please visit www.renaissance.com. Accelerated
Reader, AR, the Accelerated Reader Logo, and ATOS are trademarks of Renaissance
Learning, Inc. and its subsidiaries, registered common law or applied for in the U.S.
and other countries. Used under license.

Ben's Jerk Chicken Van

Cath Jones

Illustrated by Mia Underwood

Ransom

Ben needs cash.

He needs a job.

Ben is good at lots of things.

He can fix things
and he can cook.

Can he get a job?

Ben looks for a job.

He looks and looks.

He waits and waits.

But he cannot get a job.

Ben is sad.

"It will get better. I will get a job."

But no.

He cannot get a job.

Ben gets a van.

Now he is a man with a van!

He gets the words **Ben's Jerk Chicken** on his van.

Ben cooks chicken.

Ben can cook good chicken.

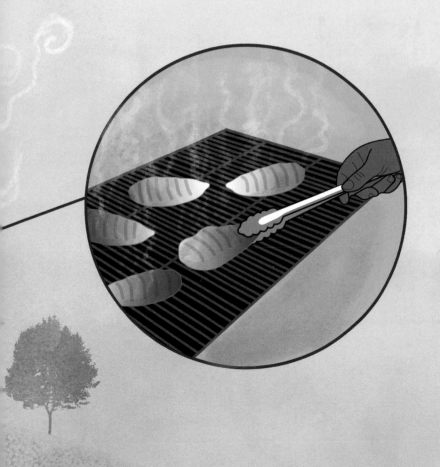

Ben cooks lots of chicken.

He cooks chicken legs.

He cooks chicken wings.

He cooks chicken
with peppers.

He cooks jerk chicken.

He cooks and cooks
and cooks.

His cat gets fat!

Ben gets nutmeg,
peppercorns and hot peppers.

He chops them up.

Into this mix go corn-fed
chicken wings.

Ben waits.
Then he lights the coals.

Then he cooks the hot
chicken in tinfoil
on the hot coals.

Quick, turn the chicken!
He cannot let it burn!

Then the chicken can go in a big pot with a lid.

The chicken will keep hot in the pot.

It is summer. In summer
Ben will sell lots of chicken.

Ben can park his van on
the road, near to the shops.

Ben cooks and sings.

"Ben's jerk chicken, yum!
Yum! Yum! Quick! Get it hot!"

He cooks lots of chicken
and waits for the rush.

Are the chicken wings good?
Sure they are!

Val and her pal see the van.

They get Ben's jerk chicken and Ben gets lots of cash.

Now Ben has a job!

Ben gets a big banner
for the top of his van.

But he falls off the ladder.
"Ow! That hurt!"

Now Ben is in bed.

He has a bad back.
He cannot cook for six weeks.

Ben's jerk chicken van is shut.

Will Val and her pals miss the Jamaican jerk chicken man?

Yes.

Val is sad.

Ben waits in bed for his back to get better.

He looks at lots of cook books.

He sees a goat dish and a fish dish.

Tap, tap, tap.

Val is at his door.

Ben is in bed, but his door is not shut.

They chat.

Val gets in Ben's van and gets the jerk chicken gear.

She lights the coals, turns on the hob and cooks chicken.

She waits for the rush.

She gets lots of cash for Ben!

Now Ben is better.

He gets a bigger, longer van.

Toot, toot, toot!

Ben and his van park up.

Val joins him and they cook and chat.

But Ben will not cook jerk chicken. Val can do that!

No, he will cook goat
– and a fish dish too.
Jamaican goat. Yum!

Now they sit in the moonlight and Ben sings to Val.

Val looks at Ben.

Ben looks at Val.

**(NOT)
THE END!**

Have you read?

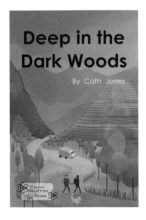

Deep
in the Dark Woods

by Cath Jones

Night Combat

by Stephen Rickard

Have you read?

G B H

by Jill Atkins

Steel Pan Traffic Jam

by Cath Jones

Ben's Jerk Chicken Van
Word count **481**

Covers:
Letters and Sounds Phase 3

Phonics

Phonics 1 Not Pop, Not Rock
Go to the Laptop Man
Gus and the Tin of Ham

Phonics 2 Deep in the Dark Woods
Night Combat
Ben's Jerk Chicken Van

Phonics 3 GBH
Steel Pan Traffic Jam
Platform 7

Phonics 4 The Rock Show
Gaps in the Brain
New Kinds of Energy

Book bands

Pink Curry!
Free Runners
My Toys

Red Shopping with Zombies
Into the Scanner
Planting My Garden

Yellow Fit for Love
The Lottery Ticket
In the Stars

Blue Awesome ATAs
Wolves
The Giant Jigsaw

Green Fly, May FLY!
How to Start Your Own
Crazy Cult
The Care Home

Orange Text Me
The Last Soldier
Best Friends